ELECTRIC CARS

by Nancy Dickmann

raintree
a Capstone company — publishers for children

Raintree is an imprint of Capstone Global Library Limited, a company incorporated in England and Wales having its registered office at 264 Banbury Road, Oxford, OX2 7DY – Registered company number: 6695582

www.raintree.co.uk
myorders@raintree.co.uk

Edited by Carrie Sheely
Designed by Cynthia Della-Rovere
Original illustrations © Capstone Global Library Limited 2021
Picture research by Eric Gohl
Production by Katy LaVigne
Originated by Capstone Global Library Ltd
Printed and bound in India

978 1 3982 0379 2 (hardback)
978 1 3982 0378 5 (paperback)

British Library Cataloguing in Publication Data
A full catalogue record for this book is available from the British Library.

Acknowledgements
We would like to thank the following for permission to reproduce photographs: Capstone Studio: Karon Dubke, 21 (bottom); Department of Energy: afdc.energy.gov, 19; Shutterstock: Art Konovalov, 5, Bartolomiej Pietrzyk, 12, David Tonelson, 15, Dmytro Zinkevych, 14, Felix Mizioznikov, 13, Mike's Spirits, 21 (top), mujijoa79, 11, North Monaco, cover, back cover, PP77LSK, 9, ra2studio, background (electronics), RomanSt-Photographer, 17 (top), ssuaphotos, 7, Sundry Photography, 17 (bottom), Yauhen_D, 6, 8

Every effort has been made to contact copyright holders of material reproduced in this book. Any omissions will be rectified in subsequent printings if notice is given to the publisher.

All the internet addresses (URLs) given in this book were valid at the time of going to press. However, due to the dynamic nature of the internet, some addresses may have changed, or sites may have changed or ceased to exist since publication. While the author and publisher regret any inconvenience this may cause readers, no responsibility for any such changes can be accepted by either the author or the publisher.

Contents

Words in **bold** are in the glossary.

What electric cars do

A car goes down the street. But you don't hear any sound! Why? It's an electric car!

Most cars burn **petrol** or **diesel** to run. Electric cars don't use petrol or diesel. They use electric power, or **electricity**, to run. They are quieter than petrol or diesel cars.

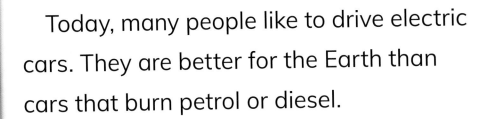

Today, many people like to drive electric cars. They are better for the Earth than cars that burn petrol or diesel.

waste gases

A petrol or diesel car sends out waste gases. Some of these are bad for the Earth. They make the planet hotter. Other kinds make the air dirty. Electric cars don't send out waste gases.

Look Inside

How do electric cars run? The power comes from a **battery** pack. Batteries store **energy**. They turn energy into electricity. The pack is made up of many batteries.

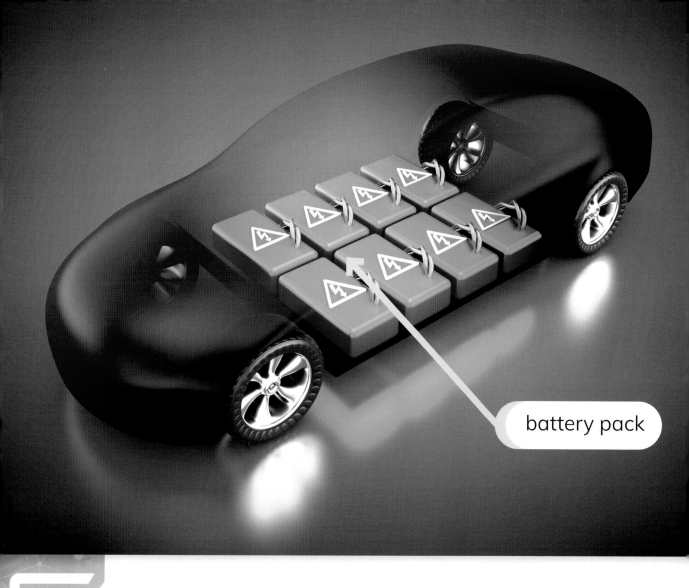

battery pack

Many toys use small batteries. Electric cars need big ones! The battery pack is very heavy. It is on the bottom of the car.

Lift the **bonnet**! There is no fuel engine. There is an electric motor instead. It uses power from the battery pack. It starts spinning. It sends power to the wheels. The wheels turn. The car goes. The faster the car goes, the more power it uses.

bonnet

electric motor

Driving uses up the battery power. A **gauge** shows drivers how much power is left. When the power runs out, the car must be plugged in so the battery pack can **charge**.

battery power gauge

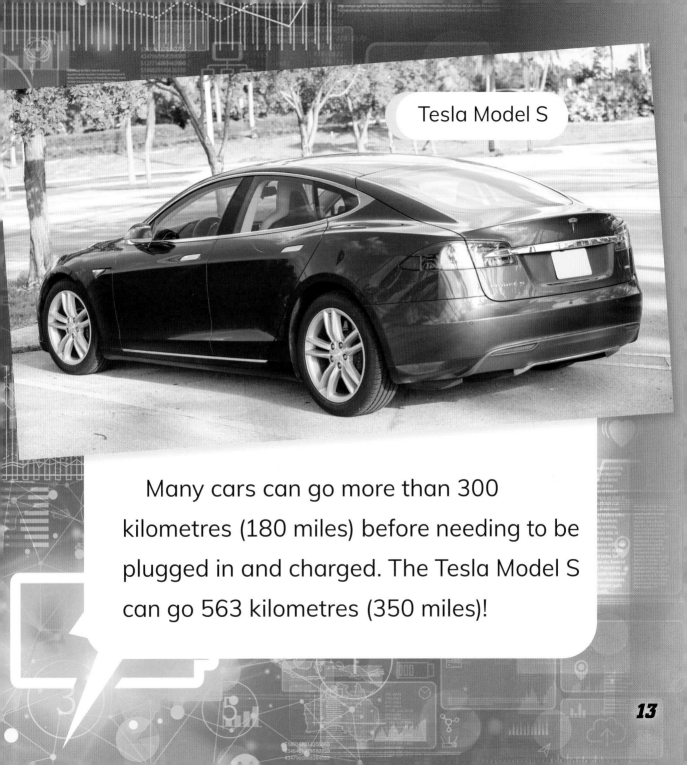

Tesla Model S

Many cars can go more than 300 kilometres (180 miles) before needing to be plugged in and charged. The Tesla Model S can go 563 kilometres (350 miles)!

LOOK OUTSIDE

How do you charge the car? There is a flap on the outside of the car. This is where the charging cord plugs in. The cord's other end connects to a plug **socket** or charger.

electric cars plugged in at chargers

People can charge their cars at home. Sometimes they need charging on the go. Some petrol stations have chargers for electric cars. Some car parks do too.

One of these cars is electric. The other uses petrol. Can you spot the difference? Look below the bumper. One car has exhaust pipes. Its petrol engine makes waste gases. The gases come out of the exhaust pipe. The electric car has no exhaust pipe. It doesn't need one!

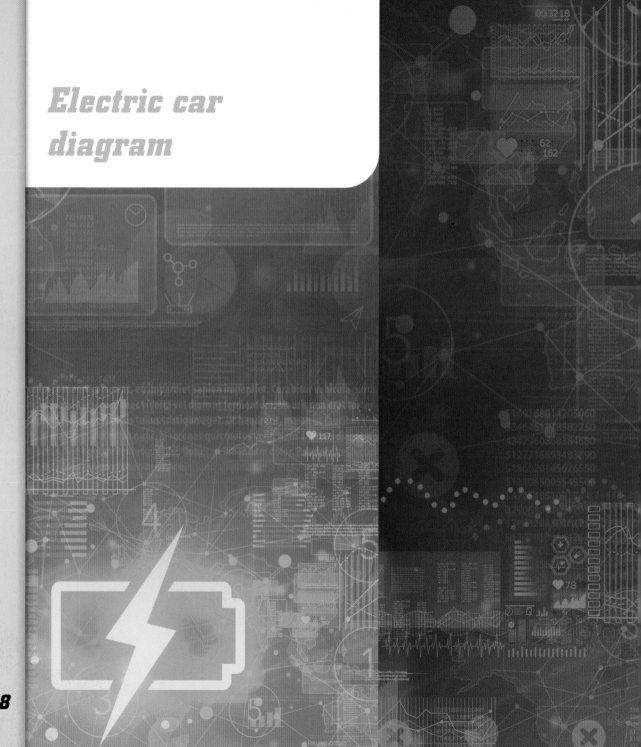

Electric car diagram

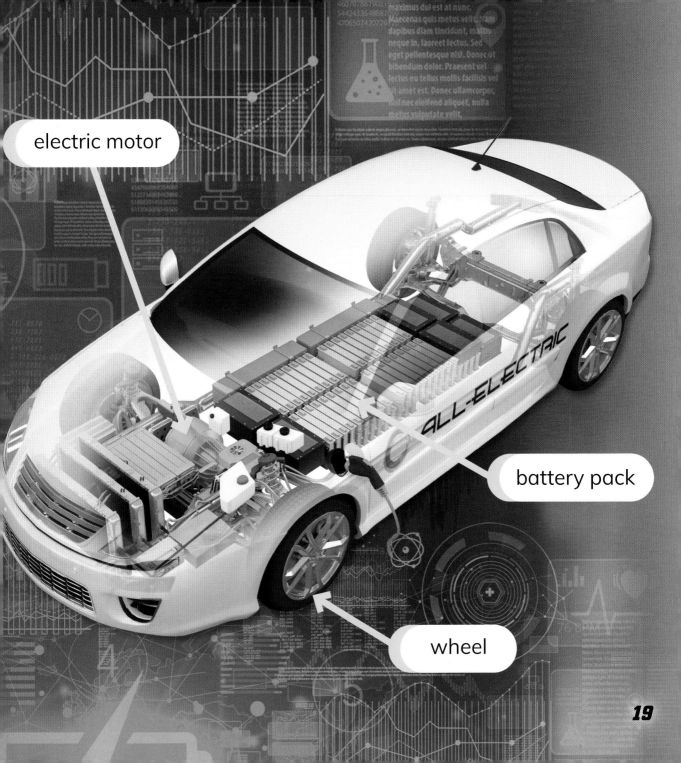

electric motor

battery pack

wheel

ALL-ELECTRIC

Go on a battery hunt

All batteries store energy. Toys often use batteries. So do many other things. Look around your home. How many things can you find that use batteries? Make a list.

Some batteries can be recharged. Others cannot. Look at your list. Ask an adult if any of the batteries in it can be recharged. If the battery can be recharged, draw a tick on your list. If it can't, draw a cross.

X   remote control
X   clock
    toy car
    torch
✓ mobile phone
   watch
✓ laptop

Glossary

battery container that stores energy and releases it as electricity

bonnet part of a car's body over the engine

charge pass electricity through something to make it more powerful

diesel heavy oil used in diesel vehicle engines

electricity flow of energy; electricity can be used to make machines work

energy strength and ability to do something

gauge instrument used to measure something

petrol liquid that is often burned in vehicle engines

socket place where an electronic device can be plugged in to supply electricity to it

Find out more

Books

Car Science: A White-knuckle Guide to Science in Action, Richard Hammond (DK Children, 2011)

How Electric and Hybrid Cars Work (Eco Works), Louise Spilsbury (Franklin Watts, 2017)

Making a Circuit (It's Electric!), Chris Oxlade (Raintree, 2013)

Website

www.bbc.co.uk/newsround/46295799
Read this BBC Newsround article for more information on electric cars.

Index